D0982613

MIND-BENDERS

by the same author

50 Wit-Sharpeners
50 Mathematical Puzzles and Oddities
Puzzles and Teasers

MIND-BENDERS

Nicholas E. Scripture

FABER AND FABER
3 Queen Square
London

First published in 1971
by Faber and Faber Limited
3 Queen Square London WC1
Printed in Great Britain by
Latimer Trend & Co Ltd Plymouth
All rights reserved

ISBN 0 571 09538 0

The title *Mind-Benders* is used with
the permission of International Mensa
and Intermensa Limited

The following puzzles are reprinted by
permission of IPC Magazines Ltd. :
Nos. 15, 20, 21, 31, 33, 37

CONTENTS

Mathematical Puzzles

Logical Puzzles

Word Puzzles

Literary Puzzles

Miscellaneous Puzzles

Solutions

MATHEMATICAL PUZZLES

1 · The Secondhand Bookshop

For many years Ashley's Secondhand Bookshop has been one of the more interesting features of Bridgington, and I usually look in once or twice a week. Consequently, it was an occasion of regret when I went along to the Closing Sale the other day. Old Mr. Ashley himself was retiring, and the volume of sales was insufficient to attract anyone else to carry on the business.

When I arrived, a lot of the stock had already been cleared, and the shelves were almost audibly sighing with relief at being so lightly laden. My attention was attracted to one shelf in particular, which offered a number of very old and out-of-date paperbacks. Each one was priced at a certain number of pence, and no two prices were the same. The thing that caught my eye, however, was the curious fact that, if one multiplied the prices of the first, second and third books in the row together, the result was just half of what one obtained by multiplying the prices of the second, third and fourth books. Even more strangely, the same thing occurred when taking the second, third and fourth books—the result was half of multiplying the prices of the third, fourth and fifth books.

In fact, this peculiarity continued through the whole row of books on the shelf! Since the prices were as low as they could be under these conditions, how many books were there, at most, and what were their prices?

2 · The Two Trains

Two trains, going in opposite directions, passed each other on adjacent tracks. The train going to Bromham was four carriages long, while the train coming from Bromham was just twice that length. On the other hand, the short train was travelling at twice the speed of the other.

If it takes 30 seconds for the two trains to pass each other,

   (i) How long will the trains take to pass each other if they exchange speeds, so that the short train halves its speed, while the longer train doubles its rate of progress?

  (ii) How long will the trains take to pass each other if they maintain the original speeds, but if the train coming from Bromham is only half as long as originally?

3 · Going to the Match

Paul and Garry had both intended to go to see the Final of the Southern Boroughs League at Bromham by bike, but the day before the match Paul twisted his ankle, and arranged to go by train.

Unfortunately, this was only the start of the boys' misfortunes! They both set out from Bridgington at the same time, Paul by train and Garry on his bicycle—and by the most extraordinary set of accidents they also arrived at Bromham at the same time.

Paul's train started out on time, and made a steady average speed of 60 m.p.h. as far as Crimpley. Here, however, the train went off the rails due to some faulty points and, while none of the passengers was injured, they were none of them particularly pleased at having to complete their journey by taxi.

Garry, cycling along at a steady 20 m.p.h., got a puncture when only a third of the way to Crimpley. There was no time to repair the damage if he wished to get to the match, so he left the machine in a barn by the side of the road, intending to come along on the following day to pick it up. He was lucky enough to catch a bus virtually immediately, and consoled himself with the thought that at least he was travelling twice as fast as on his bike, and that the bus-route went right past the Bromham Wanderers' ground.

Although the road from Bridgington to Crimpley was a mere four miles, the train journey covered three times this distance. Given that Paul's taxi-driver covered the ground at a steady 45 miles an hour, how far is it from Crimpley to Bromham?

4 · The Party

There were quite a number of people in the Clubhouse of the Gadabout Flying Club last night, and it turned into a very pleasant little party. Apart from twenty-six of the Gadabouts themselves, there were also a number of visitors from the local Motor Racing Club, and a few odd characters who were drinking companions of the fliers.

It was rather a pity that eight of the fliers were booked to do some night flying, for this meant that they were unable to drink, and another flier (who also happened to be a member of the Motor Racers) never drank anyway. However, there were still twenty-six people drinking at the party, although half of the Motor Racers present were teetotal, and those of them who did drink were also fliers.

None of the eight who were night-flying were Motor Racers, and there were forty people altogether at the party. How many were members of both the Gadabouts and the Racers, and were drinking as well?

5 · Whose Hat?

Although the party which they had held the previous evening had been quite modest, both as to the number of guests and the amount of alcohol consumed, Mike and Sheila felt that it had been quite a success.

This impression was confirmed when two of the four men who had arrived at the party wearing hats had telephoned to say that each had left with a hat which was not his own! The information started Mike thinking about what the chances were that all four men would have taken the wrong hats had there been sufficient drink to make all four equally indifferent as to their choice of headgear.

As soon as he had finished this little teaser, Mike remembered that one of the men who had been invited, but who had been unable to accept, also normally wore a hat —so he started on his calculations all over again!

What would be the chances of all four/five men departing with the wrong hats, and how much more likely is this to happen in the case of four men?

6 · What Next?

Normally, when a problem concerning Series is introduced in a book of puzzles, one is asked: 'What is the next number in the series 2, 6, 18, 54 . . . ?' (*Answer: 162*)

For a change: What are the next *three* numbers in the series?:

1	0	1
3	4	5
5	12	13
7	24	25
—	—	—

7 · Anything for a Change

Although Tom is as sensible as any twelve-year-old can be when crossing roads, his mother was still very worried when he first started going to the Crimpley Secondary School. In fact, she went so far as to threaten to take him to school each day, and to collect him at the end of school, and it was only her husband's insistence on the misery that Tom would undergo if she were to carry out this plan that stopped her putting it into practice.

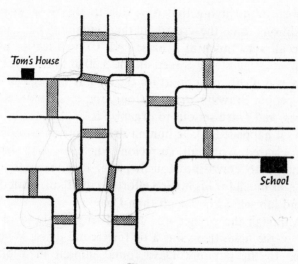

Figure 1

However, she was still very anxious, and before she finally capitulated she made Tom promise that he would always use a Pedestrian Crossing when going from one side of a road to another. Tom promised readily enough, but managed to dash out to play before his mother made him promise to use the shortest route to and from school.

Since Tom was no more keen to get to school in the

[15]

morning than any other boy of his age, what was the longest route which he could take (i.e. using the most pedestrian crossings possible), without using any crossing more than once?

Also, if Tom's mother had remembered to make him promise to take the shortest route, how many routes would he have been able to use?

8 · The Sweepstake

There was no flying that day, due to the poor weather conditions, and the crowd in the Gadabout Clubhouse were all very much at a loose end. Consequently, when someone suggested a Sweep on the 3.30 at Sandown Park there was plenty of support for the idea. It was agreed that the people drawing the first four horses should receive prizes, and Dave set out to organize it.

As it happened, Dave himself drew a horse—though he was cleared from all suspicion when his nag barely managed to crawl into fourth place. Phil received three times as much for his horse's efforts as did Paul, while Jack found himself £2 better off than Dave.

Although the winner was several lengths ahead of the rest of the field, there was a tie for second place. When it came to the pay-out, Dave found himself in a bit of trouble, for all the stake money was in five-pound notes (due to the problems in giving change when he had collected the cash). However, this was sorted out by raiding the bar till.

What was the least amount that Paul must have won, if all four winners won complete numbers of pounds?

9 · Straightforward !

It was the policy of the proprietors of the Barkwell Kennels to provide every amenity to their guests. As a result, when they bought the Small Meadow from the farm next door they decided to install sixteen kennels, since the field contained sixteen trees.

Going into the matter of expense, it was found that the cheapest way to arrange the fences was to buy straight fencing, and to have as few fences as possible. What was the least number of fences which had to be erected (N.B. the fencing was so constructed as to make it possible for two fences to cross without any trouble)?

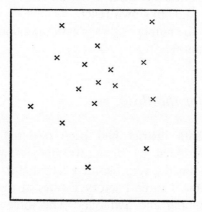

Figure 2

10 · Square Trouble

Tom was doing square roots in school, and on this particular day the maths. master had written the homework on the blackboard right at the end of the lesson. Tom had scribbled the questions down, eager to get out of the classroom, and as a result the last question was almost indecipherable.

In the end, Tom managed to make out six of the eight digits in the number which he was supposed to find the square root of. However, he could still not make out what the first figure was supposed to be (though he recalled that it was either 1, 2 or 3), and the last figure was quite beyond him.

When his father came in from work, he found Tom still poring over the problem:

$$* \ 3 \ 9 \ 4 \ 2 \ 7 \ 5 \ *$$

It was just as well that Tom had a bright father, for he was able to work out what the two indecipherable digits were, much to Tom's own relief.

What was the number (always assuming that it is in fact a perfect square)?

11 · Jobs for the Boys

The Allingham district had been declared an official Development Area by the Government, and Putemup Brothers obtained a very lucrative contract from the local Council to build three Factory Estates at the villages of Royley, Tripping and Swinbury. The three projects required labour forces of 100, 70 and 100 men respectively, apart from a certain amount of unskilled labour which could be raised in the villages themselves.

The 270 skilled workmen would have to come to the sites daily from Allington itself, and from Barham and Catterley. If Putemup Brothers actually had ninety men in each of the three towns, what is the most economical way to allocate the men to the sites, so as to keep the men's claims for travelling expenses to a minimum?

[18]

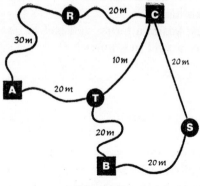

Figure 3

12 · Canned

Alan, Barry, Charles and David were queuing up for paraffin at the garage. Alan, being first, was served, and had his seven-gallon can filled. The other three, however, found that they were unlucky, since the mechanism in the pump obstinately refused to function further.

It was indeed fortunate for his three companions that Alan had merely come in order to fill his 'stand-by' can, for there was no other garage in the neighbourhood. As it was, Alan very kindly offered to let the other three have the oil, since they were actually in need of it. By the time the four men had decided among themselves as to who was most in need, the garage had closed, so they were faced with the task of sharing out the paraffin using only the cans which they had brought.

Barry had a six-gallon can, and needed only one gallon of oil, while Charles and David had a five- and a four-gallon tin respectively, and required four and two gallons of paraffin.

How many pourings were needed in order to distribute

the contents of Alan's can among the other three in the required quantities.

   (i) If Barry was in a hurry, and had to be served first;

   (ii) If Barry wasn't in a hurry?

13 · Knotted or Not?

A little teaser for those readers who may pride themselves on their visual reasoning. One of the two pieces of string shown below is knotted, while the other is not. Which is which?

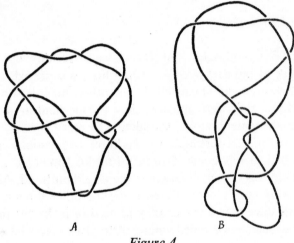

A   B

Figure 4

14 · Cheers !

In the addition sum shown on the following page, the figures have been replaced by letters, each letter representing a different digit. What were the original figures?

$$\begin{array}{c} \text{B E E R} \\ +\text{ B E E R} \\ \hline \text{D R U N K} \end{array}$$

(N.B. One may assume that beer is not odd.)

15 · Birthday Bike

Knowing what boys are, I was scarcely surprised to hear that my nephew Timothy had been plaguing his parents to give him a motor-cycle for his sixteenth birthday. What was unexpected was that he had managed to persuade them.

For weeks before the Day, he spent his spare time scanning the advertisements in the local newspapers, studying the cards outside newsagents, and generally looking around. His persistence paid off, and finally the machine was bought. It was arranged that Tim should collect it on his birthday.

Bright and early, he caught a bus, and collected his bike. Wanting to give it a fair trial, he returned home by a different route from that taken by the bus, and in fact travelled three miles farther than if he had followed the bus route.

As well as being longer, his homeward trip was along somewhat quieter roads, and he noted that the bike travelled at exactly twice the speed of the bus. As it happened, there was a slight delay on the way. The carburettor had got some dirt in it, and it took him a full quarter of an hour to strip and clean it. His parents were in a state of great anxiety by the time he returned home. In fact, had I not been at the house, and pointed out that the bus-ride alone would take him 40 minutes, I am sure they would have contacted the police.

His parents took some time to cool down, and his father made some caustic comments about the fact that he could have come home in exactly the same time had he taken the bus. Meanwhile I amused myself by working out precisely how many miles Tim had gone on his motor-cycle.

How many miles *had* he travelled on it?

16 · A Weighty Problem

Joe was a nice chap, but a rotten shopkeeper. In fact, the village store which he ran was in such a state that one day he discovered that he had lost all the weights for his scales except for those of 1 oz., 4 oz., 8 oz. and 1 lb.

If it was necessary for him to be able to weigh any number of ounces, up to and including 1 lb., how many more weights would he have had to buy had the missing weights not been discovered underneath a sack of potatoes? Also, up to what weight would he have been able to go with the assistance of his new weights?

(N.B. The extra weights would have to be as few and as small as possible, because of the expense.)

17 · Sharing

Miss Thompson was always at pains to point out the virtue of sharing, so when one of the children in her class brought her in an apple one day she naturally cut it into a sufficient number of pieces to enable each of her charges to have a taste as well as herself.

Needless to say, the pieces weren't very big, but that was not the point. She and every one of the fourteen children had a piece of apple, and it didn't matter that some portions were larger than others.

Using straight cuts only, what was the minimum number of cuts that Miss Thompson had to make? If the apple had been cored before she made the cuts, how many extra pieces could have been available if she used the same number of cuts?

18 · Mathemanian Railways

The late King Sunimsulp II of Mathemania, being a very wealthy man in his own right, decided that he could scarcely spend his money on a worthier cause than by providing a railway to link the two main towns of his little kingdom.

In spite of the fact that Mathemania is little more than a hundred miles long, Sunimsulp took great delight in

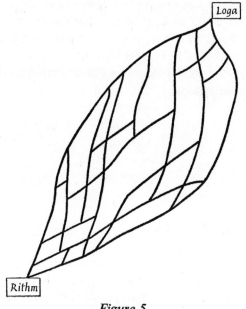

Figure 5

planning the layout (shown on the previous page), in such a way as to let the railway pass through all the most beautiful parts of his kingdom. Consequently, although there were no intermediate stations between Rithm and Loga, the system was in fact quite complex.

How many possible routes connect the two towns, assuming that the train always travels in the direction of its destination?

19 · Slot Machines

The advent of the 50p.-piece, with its seven curves, took many people by surprise. This was, of course, not merely because of the fact that this country had never had a heptagonal coin before, but also because very few of us had realized that it was possible to have a coin which was not circular yet could be used in slot machines.

If this trend were to continue, of having coins with a varying number of sides, which of the following could also be constructed so as to prevent slot machines from suffering from indigestion:

> three-sided
> eight-sided
> nine-sided
> thirteen-sided
> sixteen-sided

20 · Eleven Bags Full

There was a deep sigh of relief from everybody when the door of the bank finally closed on the back of the last customer. It was always bad on a Friday, but the Friday before a Bank Holiday was almost too bad to be true.

Everyone seemed to get a sudden urge to pay the bank a visit, and all in the last few minutes before closing.

George's sigh was one of the most heartfelt. He had not been on the counter many weeks, and he was feeling the strain. He started checking his till, and suddenly remembered that a customer had told him that one of the bags of silver he had handed in contained five shillings less than the £5 printed on the outside.

As he was a client of long-standing, George had accepted his twelve five-pound bags without question and had got busy with pen and rubber stamp. Only now did he realize that he had not asked which bag was short, and that he would have to discover this for himself.

He had more sense than to actually open the bags and start counting the contents. He pulled over the little balance and started weighing one of the bags against each of the others, and after the fifth weighing found the bag he was looking for.

With a little more thought, George could have saved himself quite a lot of trouble. The method he used to discover the bag could quite easily have involved him in ten weighings instead of five. What was the smallest number of weighing operations in which it would have been possible to find the bag which was deficient?

21 · Age of Sail

Crossing the Atlantic in small boats is now so commonplace that when Ben and his son Richard made their landfall the event caused not the slightest flurry. The seafarers took up moorings a couple of miles upstream from the mouth of the river, and after making everything shipshape aboard their craft they went ashore for a drink.

All that they wanted was to savour the taste of beer

drawn from the wood, and to feel the rolling of the solid ground beneath their feet. Had it not been for a couple of holiday-makers, resplendent in Bermuda shorts and fancy shirts, the seafarers would have had their wish. As it was, their tale was dragged out of them. They suffered their companions with some patience, until at last they felt that they had had enough.

'And how old are the two of you, then?' Asked one of the Bermuda shorts.

Old Ben looked the holiday-makers up and down. No sailors, these, he thought. 'Well, now, I'm afraid the salt air has muddled my memory a bit. All that I can remember for sure is that our combined ages come to the number of square feet of canvas that brought us across the ocean.'

Richard grinned into the secrecy of his beard. 'Oh, come now, Dad,' he said. 'You know quite well that in ten years' time I'll be as old as you were when you were twice as old as I was.'

The holiday-makers had had enough by this time, and beat a retreat. The younger of them, however, took the trouble to ask a local boatman what area of canvas the adventurers' vessel carried. Given that the answer was a 125 square feet, can *you* determine the ages of Ben and Richard?

22 · Wrong Paper

There are only four houses in Brandram Close. In spite of this, the new paper-boy managed to deliver the wrong paper to every single one, though he made no other mistakes on his round.

If each of the four households takes a different paper, in how many ways is it possible for the papers to be delivered in this way?

23 · Escape Bid !

The Governor had heard a whisper that some of his twenty-seven prisoners in the Security Wing were plotting an escape bid, although no names were mentioned.

As one of the extra precautions resulting from this rumour, the Governor laid down that prisoners were to be exercised only once a day, and then only in groups of three. Moreover, no prisoner should have the company of any other particular prisoner more often than was absolutely necessary.

If Paul exercised with Alan today, how long will he have to wait before seeing him again?

23a · Socks !

When Eileen went into hospital to have the baby, Joe had assured her that he was quite capable of looking after himself and the Twins for the few days she would be away. When it came to the push, however, it wasn't really as easy as he had imagined, and he spent the morning of her return in rushing about like a madman; plates and saucepans had piled up, windows were grimy, and dust was everywhere.

While he was doing this, he sent the boys out to play, with strict instructions as to when to be back home. They returned on time—but filthy! Into the bathroom, clean shirts, do their hair . . . then Joe realized that both of them had got their socks soaking wet! He looked at his watch, and realized that there wasn't time to change them, so he sent them straight down to get in the car, while he dashed into their room, and grabbed four socks at random from the drawer.

As it so happened, when he got into the car, and thrust the socks at them, he found that he had indeed picked out two *pairs*. Since the drawer had contained 12 blue socks, 8 grey and 6 white, all mixed up, he realized that he had been very lucky, and by the time the three of them arrived at the hospital both boys were properly be-socked.

What, in fact, were the odds against Joe's having grabbed two *pairs* of socks, as against one *pair* and two *odd-coloured* socks?

23b · Little Dogies

Chuck Bleach had been much the same as any other cowboy before Jean had agreed to marry him. When this happened, he decided that the only thing to do was for him to set up as a rancher on his own.

He had started out in a small way, but every year he found that his herd had exactly doubled in size when the round-up came along.

After round-up, Chuck always gave a party, for which he always slaughtered a cow. One year, some of the hands got rather more than usually drunk, then went into town and caused a considerable amount of damage. The Sheriff, not being particularly fond of Chuck, held him responsible, and persuaded the Judge to fine Chuck to the tune of thirteen cattle.

If Chucks herd was thus reduced to 1780 beasts, and if he had started off his ranch with the smallest number of animals that the above conditions allowed:

  (i) how many animals did he start off with? and
  (ii) how many post round-up parties had he given?

LOGICAL PUZZLES

24 · The Flirt

By the time they have reached nineteen or twenty, most boys have settled for a regular girl-friend. Not so with Joe: he was almost twenty-one, and he had six 'steadies', each of whom he saw one night in the week. In fact, the only time his family saw him was on a Sunday, half of which he spent in bed!

Talking to his mother the other day, I discovered various items of information, though I was informed that Joe never said exactly who was his steady date for any particular evening. Still, I found that he didn't see Karen on Tuesdays or Thursdays, and Mary was at evening classes on Mondays and Saturdays. Also, Anne came later in the week than did Susan, and June was always after Anne. Pauline was earlier in the week than Karen, and Mary was the day before Anne.

If, in addition, I knew that Susan was not next to Pauline, and that Karen was not next to June in the week, who did Joe take out on the various evenings of the week?

25 · Happy Families

My wife and I are very lucky, inasmuch as we get on very well with the other four couples in our block of flats. Tom Downes is an engineer, like myself, and my wife and Helen

Downes also find a great deal to talk about. One of our most regular visitors is Ann, who is somewhat of a golf-widow, and whose husband never stops trying to persuade Tom to take up golf instead of badminton. Eric and Sarah Tawley have the ground-floor flat, and the tailor has numerous cups to demonstrate his prowess at swimming.

Given that in no case does a man's Christian name have the same initial letter as his surname, and that his occupation starts with yet another letter:

 (i) What is Karen's surname?
 (ii) What is the archer's name?
 (iii) What does Mr. Elton do for a living?
 (iv) What is the doctor's favourite sport?
 (v) What is the Christian name of the policeman's wife?
 (vi) What is Mr. Palster's Christian name?
 (vii) What does Desmond do for a living?
 (viii) What are Paul's wife's names?

26 · Those Gadabouts

Tom, Dick and Harry had been spending rather a lot of time at the Gadabout Clubhouse recently, and their respective wives were beginning to murmur darkly about their being considered less important than flying. In order to try and improve relations the three men decided to surprise their spouses by arranging a little dinner one evening.

The dinner was held, and in order to prevent any possibility of the conversation turning to the rather delicate subject of flying, no one sat next to his or her spouse, and no two women sat next to each other.

Tom sat at the right of the redhead, Dick sat to the brunette's left, and Harry's wife is a blonde. What colour hair has Dick's wife?

27 · Big Business

A big American firm has representatives in England, Ireland, Scotland, Wales and France. By chance, these
gentlemen rejoiced in the names of Mr. Scott, Mr. Welsh,
Mr. English, Mr. Francis and Mr. Ireland—though none
of them resides in the country which would seem to fit
their names best.

The five men each have a particular hobby, and among
them they fly, fish, sail, and play rugger and tennis.

The representatives in both Wales and Scotland have a
natural interest in tides, and Mr. English is the angler if
Mr. Scott isn't. The man in Scotland is the angler if Mr.
Welsh is not the tennis-player. Mr. Scott regularly flies
himself from Orly to Gatwick each week-end, and Mr.
Francis is always trying to obtain a transfer so that he can
get to Wimbledon more easily.

Who is where, and does what?

28 · Two for the Price of One

Although their own children had long since grown up,
Tom and Mary Jackson still liked to keep up some of the
customs they had learnt to associate with Christmas. True,
the paper-chains had gone, and the sprigs of holly and
mistletoe had decreased in number—but there was still the
Tree.

The Tree, after all, had always been the focal-point in
their decorations. Standing in the hall, with its twinkling
lights, its tinsel and the fragile glass baubles, it was the very
epitome of the season to them.

Of course, now that the children had left home, the
presents which used to be placed at the foot of the Tree
were fewer; just a handful, in fact, which the old couple

put there for when the children next door came in to wish them both a Happy Christmas.

Usually, Mary went out and bought the presents, and wrapped them up, so that Tom could share in the children's delight and pleasure when they unwrapped them. This year, however, Tom came along with her, in order to help her carry them, so he knew what they were. However, Mary still insisted on paying for them. Tom, being inquisitive, tried to find out how much they cost, but all that he could discover was that:

(i) They had each cost a whole number of pounds;

(ii) Andrew's present had cost twice as much as Sarah's;

(iii) Frances' present was three times as expensive as Stephen's; and that

(iv) Josephine's gift had cost as much as those for Sarah and Stephen combined.

If Sarah's present was dearer than Stephen's, what was the least amount that Mary must have paid?

(N.B. For any readers who consider that the puzzle as posed is too easy: What was the least amount that Mary must have paid if Mary paid the total bill for the presents in ten-pound notes, and received no change?)

29 · Marriage Partners

The box on top of the cupboard was dusty. It was unbelievably dusty. Still, Suzanne thought as she took it down, it wasn't very surprising. It must have been five—no, six—years since she had last looked through the collection of snapshots, letters, and other oddments which it contained.

She undid the faded pink ribbon, and a small avalanche poured about her feet. One rather faded photograph fell right on top of her foot, and five young faces smiled up at her. It had been taken on graduation-day, she remembered. How they had all changed—herself as well, she thought ruefully—and the memory fluttered in the twilight. They had all five married well, though their husbands graced quite a variety of occupations, from the Navy through to Banking.

Suzanne tried to recall who had married whom. Mary, now; she and Pauline had both been very struck on a sailor—but in the end neither of them had married into the Service. In fact, Mary's husband was in the same line as was her own, and Pauline's was either a Judge or a Stockbroker.

Funny how memory is selective in what it chooses to produce, Suzanne pondered. 'I know that Catherine married the Stockbroker if Pauline didn't, and if Catherine *did* marry the Stockbroker, then Clarrie was certainly the Judge's wife, because it was either Pauline or Clarrie who had married the Judge.'

Shaking her tired old head, Suzanne replaced the snapshot with the others, and tied up the box once more, with the same faded ribbon. One of these days she really *must* get down to it, and sort these things out, she told herself.

Given that Suzanne's memory was accurate, even if it was a little fuzzy, which of the girls married whom?

30 · Crossing the Quaggy

Although Mr. Smith and Mr. Jones were on good enough terms, this amity did not extend to the feelings of their respective wives and sons. Consequently, when the recent floods swept away the bridge over the River Quaggy, a problem arose. The two families had to cross the Quaggy in order to get to market, and the only available means left to cross the river was by a small rowing-boat.

This could carry only two people at a time, so when the three Joneses and the three Smiths all arrived at the river at the same time they had to do a bit of thinking. The two men were happy enough in each other's company, but it was far too risky to permit the boys and/or wives to mix unless both men were there to keep the peace. Also, whereas all the adults were able to row, the two boys were rather too young to cope with the current.

Assuming that no one could swim, what was the quickest way for the six people to cross the Quaggy?

31 · Ring Rivals

Boxing meant a great deal to Joe. Had he ever turned professional, he would very likely have been a strong challenger for a world championship. But for him its appeal lay in its value as sport and healthy exercise, and he remained an amateur. The gym which he now ran at the back of his sports shop existed for the fun of the game.

In fact, Joe was so much opposed to the idea of even amateur championships that when four young middleweights whom he was training suggested a competition, he went to considerable trouble to side-step the proposal.

In the end he realized that he would have to allow some sort of competition, and so he arranged that each of the four young boxers should have a bout with each of the other three. In this way, he hoped, there would be the interest of competition without the element of ill-feeling which can sometimes be aroused by a knock-out tournament.

The competition was arranged so that there would be two bouts on each of three successive Saturdays. On the first Saturday Billy fought Jim, and was knocked out in Round Two. In the second week, Billy went down again, this time to Clive; but he managed to win the last of his three bouts. The other unlucky fellow who won only one of his fights was Clive; though these results were not entirely unexpected by anyone who knew the boxers.

The bout whose result was least predictable was the one between Jim and Martin, two very promising youngsters. Their meeting was awaited with keen interest. . . .

Who won this bout, and in which week of the competition was it fought?

32 · The Fairest of Them All

Rose Clark, Betty Taylor and Susan Butcher work as a secretary, a milliner and a butcher's cashier—though in no case does the girl's surname seem to tally with her occupation. Betty, the blonde, is allergic to the smell of blood, while the milliner's hair is auburn.

Each of the girls is well known for being the prettiest, the silliest, or the eldest (the last being absolutely terrified of being near anything sharp or pointed).

If the redhead is the silliest provided that the secretary isn't, what is the name of the prettiest of the three girls, and what is the colour of her hair?

33 · Dress Sense

When the members of the Ladies' Sewing Circle hold their weekly meeting, it is not, perhaps, surprising that their incidental conversation should often turn to the subject of dress, and not infrequently touch upon the clothes which fellow-members are wearing at the time.

In particular, it is their various tastes in colour that offer agreeable opportunities for comment, not the less enjoyable for the scope afforded for the occasional barbed thrust.

The most recent meeting offers a typical example of such absorbing exchanges. There were five members present. All wore outfits of blue, black, brown, or green, and each colour was worn by at least one of them. Here are some fragments of conversation overheard during the coffee-break:

'My dear, isn't it *nice* to see *dear* Mrs. Carroll out of mourning for once!'

'Did you see the *look* Mrs. Evans gave Mrs. Baker?—just because they're wearing the same colour. . . .'

'. . . *So* sensible of Mrs. Downes not to wear black or brown. Her *complexion*, you know. . . .'

'. . . And that blue suits you so, Mrs. Baker.'

'Mind, you'll never see Mrs. Archer in any shade of brown. . . .'

Who was wearing which colour outfit?

34 · Police Business

After the break-in at Johnson's Warehouse last week, the local police were soon able to establish that one of the men concerned lived in the flats just around the corner from the burgled premises, and that he was fair-haired.

Not wishing to scare their man away, they sent Police-woman Jenkins to the flats in order to ascertain the man's name. Unfortunately, the Officer concerned had not been in the Force long enough to learn the official technique, with the result that she came back with an assortment of information.

Apparently, the families living in the flats rejoiced in the names of Paynter, Baker and Taylor, and the occupations of the three men were actually those of artist, baker and tailor—but Jenkins had no idea as to who was what, except that she was sure that no man's job coincided with his name. Likewise, the men's first names were Tom, Dick and Harry, but it was anyone's guess as to which name fitted which surname!

The only other two scraps of information obtained were that Tom (the black-haired artist) played golf with Mr. Taylor sometimes, and the Policewoman had overheard Dick's wife telling Mrs. Paynter that she couldn't stand red hair . . . though Jenkins managed to find that one of the men in the house actually did have red hair.

Luckily, Inspector O'Brien, who was in charge of the case, was quite astute, so he was able to work out his suspect's name. Can you?

35 · Santa's Sleigh

Due to increased pressure of work, Santa decided that the old sleigh, which he had used for more years than he cared to remember, was too small. Consequently, when the reindeer came along on Christmas Eve, all prepared to be harnessed into the four-pair harness which they expected, they were faced with a brand-new streamlined creation, with a 'line-ahead' harness.

This gave rise to some trouble among the eight deer. For a start, only Prancer and Bluebell were used to leading the way, while Thunderbird, Dancer and Twinkle always caused trouble if any two of them were harnessed next to each other.

As if these complications were not enough, Sugar-lump, Twinkle and Jeremy considered it beneath their dignity to be among the last four, while Dancer had to be harnessed between Jeremy and Snowflake if a show of temperament was to be avoided—though Jeremy tended to be jumpy if harnessed immediately behind Twinkle on account of the fact that he had received a black eye from Twinkle's hoof on one occasion.

How did Santa harness the reindeer, if he had to take all the above into consideration, and if he also let Snowflake and Prancer be harnessed next to each other on account of their being twins?

36 · Clubland

Chessletbury is one of those rarities: a village which has managed to remain relatively isolated and more or less unspoilt by the prevalent eczema of subtopian sprawl.

As a result, of course, there is comparatively little in the way of commercial entertainment in the village, with the consequence that every man in the little community is an active member in at least one of the four main organizations. Half of the male population, for instance, find that membership of the Drama Society, or of the British Legion, or of the Rifle Club takes all the free time at their disposal, while a quarter of the men belong to the Oddfellows.

In addition, those enthusiasts who belong to both the Drama Society and to the British Legion also belong to at least one of the other organizations as well, while a seventh of the total number of men find that the combination of Rifle Club and Drama Society or the Rifle Club and the British Legion leaves them no time for anything else.

Of the super-enthusiasts who belong to the Rifle Club, the Drama Society *and* the British Legion, only Paul Abercrombie finds that he has also sufficient time to belong to the Oddfellows—possibly because he is the only one of the seven who is a bachelor!

What is the male population of Chessletbury?

37 · Blondes, Brunettes, or Redheads?

In the beginning, Bill's Stag Party was going to be a simple occasion for a few close friends to meet at the local for a drink. However, things escalated. He had kept very quiet at the office about his approaching wedding, but the news had slipped out, and several men from the office turned up. Again, his best man usually met a few of his own friends on a Friday evening, so they arrived as well.

In short, the party assumed such proportions that when Bill was asked next day how many people had been there, the only numbers he could recall were the results of a poll concerning the company's tastes in girl-friends.

For example: Six of those present had liked red-heads, and these six were also among the twenty-two who liked blondes. However, not all those who liked blondes had any time for redheads or brunettes. In fact, seven of them stated categorically that they had no time for anyone who wasn't a blonde. On the other hand, there were three stalwarts who gave voice to the opinion that brunettes were the only girls worth bothering about, though at some time or another sixteen of the men present had had brunette girl-friends.

Although Bill could remember only this, a little thought revealed that he had enough information to determine how many men there had been at the party; and he was also able to calculate how many of them liked all girls, regardless of whether they were blonde, brunette, or redhead!

What were these numbers?

38 · Identikit

Although the idea of using 'Identikit' pictures is now widespread, the police at Bigglesberry had been using the technique for a dozen or more years before the official scheme came into operation. Inspector O'Brien had a friend who was the Art Master in the Bigglesberry Secondary School, and this man had made up a set of drawings on plastic sheet so that a composite face could be made up out of any combination of ten hair-styles, ten pairs of eyebrows, ten pairs of eyes, and so on with noses, mouths and chins as well.

Of course, this was not used 'officially', but on numerous occasions the device was instrumental in helping to clear up crimes which otherwise would have remained on the 'dead' book. For instance, there was the time when old Mrs. Jackson, who ran the sub-Post Office in Bigglesberry High Street, was attacked by a man, and was robbed of over £400.

True, Mrs. Jackson's eyes weren't all that they might have been, and when she was shown the Identikit she wasn't too sure of being able to piece together the face of the man who had robbed her. However, with a bit of encouragement, she did manage to narrow the field down a bit, as shown in the following table:

Hair	either no.	3, 4, or 6
Eyebrows	,,	1, 2, 5, or 7
Eyes	,,	1, 3, 4, or 8
Nose	,,	4, 6, or 7
Mouth	,,	2, 3, 5, or 9
Chin	,,	1, 3, 4, or 7

In addition, Inspector O'Brien was able to obtain the following pieces of information:

(i) The numbers of the eyebrows and mouth were the same (and in fact this was the only case which Mrs. Jackson felt that any numbers matched);

(ii) If, and only if, the nose-number was less than the hair-number, then the eyebrows-number was certainly more than the hair-number;

[40]

(iii) If, and only if, the nose-number was higher than the hair-number, then the eyes-number came in between the nose- and hair-numbers; and,

(iv) The nose-number was 7, if (and only if) the mouth-number was less than the chin-number.

From this information, and numerous cups of tea, the Inspector was able to produce a picture which proved to fit the culprit exactly, and was of great assistance in tracking him down.

What were the numbers of the various parts of the robber's face?

39 · The New Teacher

It is only to be expected that a class of normally healthy children will tend to try to 'play up' a new teacher. However, when Mr. Jones was first exposed to the mercies of 3C he considered that five of the children were just that bit *too* aggravating.

The trouble was—what to do! In the end, he decided that the best course of action would be to take the names of the five culprits, and report them to the Headmaster, and he set out to do just this.

The first child he asked informed him that Tom's surname was Smith, and that Susan and Mary were respectively Smith (again) and Robinson. The next child said that while Mary's name was indeed Robinson, Susan's was actually Jones, as was Jim's. Finally, another member of the class confused the issue still further by informing the teacher that Mary's name was really Brown, that Jim's was Jones, and that Charlie's parents were Mr. and Mrs. Harris.

Assuming that each of the three informants actually told the truth once, and lied twice, that all the five culprits did in fact have different surnames, and that Mr. Jones knew that Jones was the surname of either Susan or Mary —who was who?

40 · Bridge Fiends

When Inspector O'Brien first came to Bigglesberry he made it his business to find out as much as he could about the more notable of the inhabitants. In order to do this, he found that an occasional visit to the Bigglesberry Arms most useful.

The first time he went there, the Landlord was a little suspicious of his motives, and although he answered his questions, he did not put himself out to do so. Thus, when the Inspector inquired about the four men playing a hand of bridge at a corner table, these were the scraps of information which he gleaned:

Bill was partnering Dennis, who was on the right of the bald-headed man. The solicitor was on Joe's right, and the Town Clerk was the dark-haired man. Bill was either the fair-haired or the red-haired man, while the doctor was to the left of the Town Clerk's partner. Finally, Tom's partner was either the solicitor or the undertaker, and Tom himself was the man sitting on the right of the red-haired man.

What was the Inspector able to make of these tid-bits?

41 · The Navigators

As is the case with most good Flying Clubs, the Gadabouts hold an Annual Competitions Week. There are prizes for Spot Landings, Aerobatics, and so on, but the real highlight is the Navigation Test.

This particular Test, for various reasons, is open only to the top eight fliers, as determined by the results of the other Competitions. Consequently, the order in which the competitors emerge is, to all intents and purposes, the Club's Hierarchy for the ensuing year.

This year, the standard set was extremely high, and although I have mislaid my official Result Sheet, I can remember the following points:

George was sandwiched between Arthur and Harry; Harry came lower in the ranking than did Eric, as long as Bill was in the first four; Bill won his bet that he would be at least three places higher than Dave, but at least Dave managed to beat Fred, who was in turn consoled by the fact that his twin brother Eric just managed to beat Arthur; Fred was sandwiched between Dave and Charlie, and either Arthur or Charlie occupied the eighth place in the final ranking.

What was the final order of the competitors?

WORD PUZZLES

42 · Double Acrostic (I)

This particular type of puzzle lies somewhere between the pun and the crossword puzzle. In essence, it consists of a set of clues similar to those of a crossword; however, instead of the answers to the clues fitting together in a two-dimensional matrix, the link consists of the fact that the initial letters of the answers, followed by the final letters (the 'Uprights'), provide the answer to yet another clue. For example:

> UPRIGHTS: It's nice to have this underfoot,
> though it's not so nice to be on it.
>
>   (i) Find a fish
> (ii) Fish for a find
> (iii) A body of men
>   with a Colonel behind.

43 · Double Acrostic (II)

> UPRIGHTS: To its Flowers, lament's no stranger,
> To watch for its fires, it oft has a ranger.
>   (i) Just like the air
> (ii) All surrounded by sand
> (iii) They call it this
>   when things get out of hand.

44 · Double Acrostic (III)

> UPRIGHTS: The lack of this for even a while
>   Would cause no journalist to smile.
>
> (i) A sorrowful rip
> (ii) But yet most ascetic
> (iii) Caress
> (iv) Obliterate
>   (v) Its victims pathetic.

45 · Andrew's Puzzle

The Acrostic which follows makes no pretence to any rhyme in its clues, but in spite of this it is still a genuine example of the genre. Though it lacks polish, I am delighted to include it on account of its source. My son, Andrew, insisted on my explaining what I was doing while constructing the previous acrostics; having just learnt how to use a dictionary, Andrew then constructed this example of an acrostic by himself (—the reason for my delight lies in the fact that Andrew was not yet eight at the time!).

> UPRIGHTS: Used for swimming.
> (i) Collapse
> (ii) Cottage
> (iii) To suffer
> (iv) Kind of sausages.

46 · Triple Acrostic

For those who find Double Acrostics too simple, the following may prove more to their taste. The only difference lies in the fact that in a Triple Acrostic the initial letters of the answers to the clues are followed by the *middle* letters, and *then* by the final letters.

UPRIGHTS: Fly-by-night salesman, maybe a fake,
            Or a cheap politician on the make.
  (i) Galloping horses
  (ii) Lessening storm
  (iii) Repay the cash
  (iv) Usual form.

47 · Twisted Triple Acrostic

In order to appease any crossword fans who have found
the previous acrostics too easy, this final example has been
given a slight twist. Although it is basically a straight-
forward Triple Acrostic, the answers to alternate clues are
written from right to left, instead of the usual left to right.

  (i)   She's an old-fashioned girl . . .
  (ii) . . . who never cares to give her name;
  (iii)   He is just plain simple. . . .
  (iv) . . . Her England was a place of fame;
  (v)   These also were royal. . . .
           UPRIGHTS: make washdays a game.

48 · Word Ladders

It usually takes a certain amount of time and trouble to
change something that is *wet* so that it becomes *dry*. If
merely *words* are involved, however, the process is far
more simple.

Taking one of the words, change a single letter so as to
make another recognizable word, and continue the process
until the second word is arrived at. Thus, for example:
WET—WEY—WRY—DRY.

Can you, in a similar way, turn FOOT into SHOE, and
WOOD into COAL, both in only three 'steps'? If these are too
easy, try stretching a FOOT into a YARD, and turning over a

new LEAF so as to become GOOD (for these, you may allow yourselves four 'steps' to complete the transformation).

49 · Vocabulary (I)

In this, and the two puzzles following, the asterisks represent missing letters (e.g. the answer to the first clue is ENTIRETY).

E N T * * * * (completeness)
* E N T * * * (done in the head)
* * E N T * * * (final)
* * * E N T * * (joined firmly)
* * * * E N T * (offers)
* * * * * E N T (poisonous)

50 · Vocabulary (II)

T O N * * * * * (relation in key)
* T O N * * * * (petroleum)
* * T O N * * * (amaze)
* * * T O N * * (philosophical)
* * * * T O N * (whetstone)
* * * * * T O N (do up again)

51 · Vocabulary (III)

M E N * * * * * (mind)
* M E N * * * * (correction)
* * M E N * * * * (make insane)
* * * M E N * * * (disembodied spirit)
* * * * M E N * * (first principles)
* * * * * M E N * (feeling)
* * * * * * M E N (not as keen on redheads)

[47]

52 · Word Square (I)

As with clothes, puzzles also have their fashions. This particular type enjoyed great popularity between the wars, and is showing signs of making a come-back in the last couple of years. In the following specimens, the four clues result in a square of four letters, the words across reading the same as those down.

1. Exhausted
2. Composition
3. Religious
4. Essence

53 · Word Square (II)

1. Shallow vessels
2. River
3. Flaring star
4. Break

(CLUE: This square consists of two words, and their reversals.)

54 · Word Square (III)

1. Bad
2. Loathsome
3. Evils
4. Inferior

(CLUE: This revolting puzzle leaves more than a score of letters unused.)

55 · Word Square (IV)

1. Pound
2. Entire
3. Appease
4. Horse-cloth
5. Fold

56 · Word Square (V)

1. Vertical
2. Wash-basin
3. Part of the palate
4. Gourd
5. Mark

57 · Word Square (VI)

As any crossword fan realizes, such puzzles may be divided into two main categories, 'Simple' or 'Primitive', and 'Complex' or 'Cryptic'. In order to satisfy those readers who prefer the Cryptic type to the Primitive, I have included the following two Cryptic Word Squares.

1. The aim—a holy man and his vestment.
2. Dance as though pickled.
3. Works—even a comic one may end tragically.
4. If these fairies could cope, they'd be able to see what went on above.
5. Destroy a region after an age.

58 · Word Square (VII)

1. Establish a factory . . .
2. . . . where Americans would employ this.
3. To lower a support.
4. Informers approved of by Quoodle.
5. Trestle rests uncomfortably.

LITERARY PUZZLES

59 · A Square Quotation

The square below contains a well-known quotation taken from the 'Elegy Written In A Country Churchyard', by Thomas Gray (1716–71).

In order to discover the passage, start with the E in the bottom left-hand corner, and proceed by taking a letter next to it, either to the side or on the top or below.

O	W	C	E	D	T	H	E
R	R	O	L	I	F	E	R
R	E	F	L	A	O	D	U
A	V	E	R	L	R	A	T
N	S	I	T	E	E	F	H
C	H	H	S	L	M	R	E
A	I	N	L	H	A	S	O
E	P	E	E	E	H	T	F

60 · Characters

The following characters or objects have all been created by writers, either in prose or verse. What are the names of their creators?

Roger Brook; The C-chute; Jane Eyre; Toad;
the Yonghy-Bonghy-Bo; Mrs. Worthington;
Fu Manchu.

(CLUE: The initials of the first names of the writers,

taken in the above order, give the surname of one of the greatest novelists this country has ever produced.)

61 · Hexagonal Quotation

The word hexagon below consists of a quotation from the *Confessions* of St. Augustine. The first letter of the passage is one of the six adjoining the asterisk in the centre.

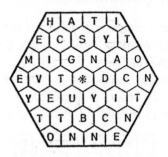

In order to spell out the quotation, proceed by taking one of the letters adjoining. (This gives anything up to six possibilities, making it rather more interesting than the possible four offered in the 'Square Quotation'. However, if anyone needs a clue, I will go so far as to mention that the passage is in the form of a request.)

62 · Colours

The following colours appear in the titles of works written by the list of authors given (though not necessarily given in the same order as the colours). What are the full titles of the works, and by which of the authors were they produced?

Black; Purple; Scarlet; Golden; White; Green; Silver.

James G. Frazer; John Galsworthy; Conan Doyle; H. E. Bates; Robert L. Stevenson; D. H. Lawrence; Emlyn Williams.

63 · Numbers

In the previous problem, dealing with colours, there were seven colours given, and seven authors. Here is another similar puzzle, only this time numbers are given instead of colours. Also, in order to make things a little more interesting, although there are again seven authors, there are only six numbers given!

What are the full titles of the books, and who wrote which?

Two; Three; Four; Five; Seven; Thirty-Nine.

Compton Mackenzie; John Buchan; Arnold Bennett; Edgar Wallace; Anton Chekhov; T. E. Lawrence; Thomas Hardy.

64 · Tetrahedral Quotation

The illustration below shows the 'net' of a tetrahedron, or a triangular pyramid. When the tetrahedron is erected, one can trace out a famous definition of 'What is News!', as given by Charles A. Dana in the New York *Sun*.

65 · Nautical Quotation

This final 'Quotation' puzzle is dealt with in the same manner as the 'Hexagonal' and 'Tetrahedral' puzzles. Unlike the 'Tetrahedral', a clue is given as to the start of the passage (one of the letters adjoining the asterisk), but unlike either of the other puzzles, the author's name is also concealed in the array. However, so as not to make it too difficult, the letters forming the author's name are in blocked capitals.

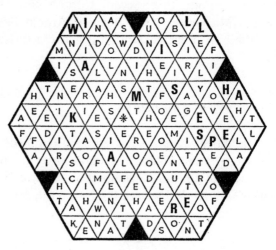

66 · Dates

This little puzzle is included for the benefit of those readers who pride themselves on their knowledge of the history of literature, and who have an eye for a bargain.

Below are six questions, each with a pair of letters preceding it. Each question is followed by three possible answers (one of which is correct), and after each answer is a pair of letters. The task is to start with the question labelled PR, proceed to the question indicated by the letters after the correct answer to PR, and so on until one arrives at RP. What is the correct route for PR to RP? (By the way, the correct route is not necessarily the shortest.)

XM   In which year did Lewis Carroll's *Alice in Wonderland* appear?

>1835 (RP)
>1865 (XR)
>1895 (XP)

PR   Two of the following appeared in 1935. Which is the odd one out?

>T. S. Eliot: *Murder in the Cathedral* (RM)
>J. Steinbeck: *Tortilla Flat* (XM)
>G. Greene: *The Power and the Glory* (XP)

RM   The first of Leslie Charteris's 'Saint' books (*The Saint Meets the Tiger*) appeared in:

>1918 (XM)
>1928 (RP)
>1938 (XR)

XP   One of the following appeared before the outbreak of the Second World War. Which one?

>*Venus Observed* (play by C. Fry) (RP)
>*The Mask of Demetrios* (thriller by Eric Ambler) (RM)
>*Across the River & Into the Trees* (Hemingway) (MX)

MX   In what year did Jean-Jacques Rousseau publish his *Confessions*?

>1751 (XR)
>1781 (RM)
>1871 (XM)

XR   The year 1495 was a milestone in printing history. With which of the following events was it concerned?

The first transatlantic press (Mexico City) (MX)
The first printing of the Buddhist Sutra (XP)
The first book was printed in Denmark (PR)

RP   Finis.

MISCELLANEOUS PUZZLES

67 · Crossword

Across
  1. Exchange a covering (4)
  4. 'Every day speaks a new scene,
      the . . . crowns the play.' (F. Quarles) (4, 3)
  8. It sounds as though a valley might take advantage (5)
 10. A learning role (4)
 11. As an owl or a Silver Cloud might glide (8)
 12. Tasty nonsense (5)
 14. (*See 22 across*)
 16. Smooth the papers (5)
 18. Short association with an idiot (3)
 19. Oriental, but a gentleman—unlike cocoa (3)
 20. Short equivalent to a double negative (3)
 22. Certainly an ungentlemanly thief (3–8)
 25. Sprinkle an ornament (5)
 26. Gas mains could be heaping up (8)
 28. Angry, I consider (5)
 31. God in a foundation carries an officer's kit (8)
 32. Rumour an address (4)
 33. To revel is a reverse—or an advantage (5)
 34. Instructed: 'Rid Beef' (7)
 35. A short literary doctor (1, 3)

Down
  1. (*See 7 down*)

2. Separate a portion (4)
3. Not as easy as it sounds, to conquer this (7)
4. Articulates imperfectly (5)
5. Strangers—or an inconsistent saint (6)
6. Comedies are rare in those in hospitals (8)
7. You could do this if you're out in the rain (5, 1, 4)
9. Mournful-sounding cloth-workers (5)
13. A vision of mirth (5)
15. Try it 'as yes' (5)
17. Place where sea heroes turn (8)
21. Tarnished and located (7)
22. One of Disney's most lovable creations (5)
23. As honour not needed with tights (6)
24. Isolate the S.E. Nile (6)
27. Shivering reeds show desire (5)
29. Real nobleman (4)
30. Little kitchens make a burlesque act (4)

68 · Twisted Crossword

Although this crossword, like the previous one, is very simple, it possesses a slight difference from the normal run of these puzzles. The distinction lies, not in the fact that the clues are any different, but in the fact that although the 'Down' clues do in fact read from top to bottom, the 'Across' clues result in answers reading from right to left instead of the normal left to right.

Across

1. Oppose (6)
4. Numbed (6)
9. Membranes (5)
10. One of a pair? (7)
11. Snow-shoe (3)
12. Large deer (3)
14. Capacity (7)
16. Fish eggs (3)
17. Stem (5)
19. Magnificent (5)
25. Vehicle (3)
27. Proceed (7)
30. Railway branch-line (3)
31. Perch (3)
32. Informal (7)
33. Jaguar (5)
34. Sea-snail (6)
35. Faults (6)

1. List (6)
2. Smoothing tool (7)
3. Sitting (7)
5. Golf club (5)
6. Follow (5)
7. Rob (6)
8. Rod (5)
13. Destiny (3)
15. Annoy (3)

18. Vase (3)
20. Open air (7)
21. Without inclination (7)
22. Song (3)
23. Requite (6)
24. Stanza (5)
26. Lapels (6)
28. Viper (5)
29. Prevent (5)

69 · Clueless

Just for a change, here is a Crossword Puzzle 'in reverse', so to speak. Normally, one is given clues (with appropriate numbers) and a framework in which to write in the answers. In this case, here are the answers to the clues (written in order, but without numbers), and the problem is to construct the framework of the puzzle, putting in the blacked-out squares and the numbers.

Answers:

ACROSS: airships, amp, via, nil, inner, drown, aides, ennui, era, tag, egg, throttle.

DOWN: asp, rover, heard, pin, navigate, landings, nod, own, sotto, ergot, ash, eve.

(N.B. The 'skeleton' is, of course, perfectly symmetrical with reference to blacked-out lights.)

70 · Reversals

To conclude the crosswords, here is one which, in spite of being extremely simple, may yet give rise to some thought.

With the exception of the words which have already

been entered, the answers to the rest of the clues are words which make sense whether they are read from left to right or from right to left. The clues below have been placed so that the answers are in alphabetical order, with no distinction as to whether they are 'across' or 'down', the clues in brackets being clues to the word produced when reading from right to left.

storehouse (drank hard)
consume (Scots toe)
cut off (old magistrate)
discharges (part of a letter)
outcast (fight off)
tangle closely (cap)
chum (flow against)
hole (upset)
tup (spoil)
renegade (sailor)
attribute (attribute)
cross (entrance)
thong (portions)
hill (decay)
total (dram)
short tradition (projectile)

71 · Hidden Countries

In the following passage, if you look carefully, you will find the names of five countries:

'When you hear that a friend has developed swollen glands or some such thing, and has had to enter hospital, you tend to forget that there are more comfortable places to be ill in. For example, some people go to a spa in search of health—though this is really feasible only when one happens to own a bank, or earns enough to keep half the female population of New York in diamonds.'

72 · Matchsticks

This is an old, old teaser, but just in case it has slipped the reader's memory. . . .

'Using six matchsticks, and not breaking any of them, how many equilateral triangles can be constructed?'

Now, for those who have come across the puzzle above previously:

'Using *twenty-seven* matchsticks, and without breaking any of them, how many *squares* can be made?'

73 · More Matchsticks

For the bargain-hunters, here are eight teasers for the price of one:

Place eight matches in the form of a square, each side of the square being two matchsticks in length, now. . . .

> (i) Rearrange four matches, so as to form *two* equal squares; then
>
> (ii) Add four matches so as to form *three* equal squares; then

(iii) Rearrange three matches so as to form *four* equal squares; then

(iv) Add four matches and rearrange two matches so as to form *five* equal squares; then

(v) Add one match and rearrange three matches so as to form *six* equal squares; then

(vi) Add five matches and rearrange two matches so as to form *seven* equal squares; then

(vii) Rearrange two matches so as to form *eight* equal squares; then

(viii) Add three matches and rearrange two matches so as to form *nine* equal squares.

74 · The End !

Depending on the taste of the reader, this final item may be regarded either as one lengthy puzzle in its own right, or else as a collection of ten small tid-bits, all offering a small morsel of entertainment. If ten puzzles are required, go right ahead; if something more meaty is desired, here are the instructions:

Below, there are ten questions, each preceded by a code-word, and each having two possible answers, of which at least one is correct. Starting at the question coded as FCPY, pick your answer, and proceed to the question whose code-word is given in brackets after the answer you have chosen, and so on until you arrive at E.

The code-words given to the questions are in fact coded versions of the names Joan, Jean, Jane, June, Sean, Sara, Saul, Nora, Neil and Nell, who are, in fact, the children of my two sisters. It so happens that my sister Anne's children all have their names attached to the questions involved in the shortest route from

FCPY to E. How many children does Anne have, and what are their names?

FPGP   A flower which blooms every six months is a
                biennial   (E)
                biannual (YCHH)

XDYC   If this 'shadow-picture' is actually of a piece of
string which goes
'under & over' itself
all the time, it is
                knotted   (YCKH)
                unknotted (XCPY)

YCHH   The solution to the alphametic 'CANT + CUT = TWEED' is
                unique   (XDYC)
                not unique (FPDH)

FCPY   A jerkin is
        a young salmon   (XCPY)
        a short coat or jacket (XDYC)

YCKH   A proditor is
                a goad   (YCHH)
                a traitor (YBGP)

XCPY   More Americans died in the American Civil War than died in the course of World War I
                true (YCKH)
                false (XPYC)

XBPY   There are as many 'points' (in the mathematical sense) along the line forming the circumference of a circle as there are in the area enclosed by the circumference.
                true (YBGP)
                false (XPYC)

FPDH   Is it impossible to have a piece of paper with only only one edge and one side?
                    yes   (FPGP)
                    no   (XBPY)

YBGP   Can a woman marry her widower's brother?
                    yes   (FPGP)
                    no   (E)

XPYC   A transcendental number is
             an irrational number   (XBPY)
             a non-algebraical number   (FPDH)

SOLUTIONS

1 · The Secondhand Bookshop

Under the set of conditions stated, there can be only six books on the shelf, their prices being 1, 3, 4, 2, 6 and 8 pence respectively.

Had the stipulation not been made that the prices were as low as possible, then the number of books could be infinite, their prices being 1, 3, 5, 2, 6, 10, 4, 12, 20, 8 pence, and so on.

2 · The Two Trains

(i) The new time will be exactly the same as before, since neither the lengths of the trains nor their speeds relative to each other have altered.

(ii) The time taken this time will be 20 seconds. The reason is, that the total lengths of the two trains is now only $\frac{2}{3}$ of the original, so the time taken will be only $\frac{2}{3}$ of the original.

3 · Going to the Match

Paul's train ride took twelve minutes. If the distance from Crimpley to Bromham is X miles, then it took Paul a further $\frac{4X}{3}$ minutes to complete his journey.

Garry spent only four minutes on his bike, then another four minutes on the bus before he arrived at Crimpley. In order to complete the trip, the bus took a further $\frac{3X}{2}$ minutes.

From the above, since both boys took the same time on their journey:

$$12 + \frac{4X}{3} = 4 + 4 + \frac{3X}{2}$$

Hence, $24 + 8X = 9X$, or $X = 24$ *miles*.

4 · The Party

The drinkers who were both Fliers and Motor Racing enthusiasts must have numbered six.

5 · Whose Hat?

In the case of four men wearing hats, the total possible number of ways in which the hats could be taken is 24, of which there are 9 ways in which no hat would be taken by its proper owner.

When five men are involved, instead of four, the total number of ways in which the hats could be taken rises dramatically, to 120. However, the ways in which the five hats could all be worn by the wrong men also rises very considerably, to 44.

In consequence of these possibilities, the odds are slightly in favour of complete wrong-hattedness in the case of four men rather than that of the five, the actual probabilities being of the order of 45 to 44.

6 · What Next?

This particular Series may perhaps be best appreciated by adding the middle- and right-hand numbers, and then comparing their sum to the left-hand number. It will soon be spotted that the left-hand number is in fact the square root of the total of the other two numbers,

$$3 = \text{sq. rt. of } 9 \quad (4 + 5)$$
$$5 = \text{sq. rt. of } 25 \quad (12 + 13)$$
$$7 = \text{sq. rt. of } 49 \quad (24 + 25)$$

and also that the two numbers which have been summed are also consecutive.

Consequently, the next set of numbers in the Series will be:

$$9 \quad 40 \quad 41 \quad (9^2 = 40 + 41)$$

and the Series will continue

$$11 \quad 60 \quad 61$$
$$13 \quad 84 \quad 85 \quad \text{and so on.} \ldots$$

7 · Anything for a Change

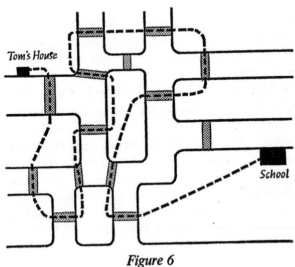

Tom's House

School

Figure 6

Although there are fourteen pedestrian crossings in the map, it is impossible for Tom to use more than twelve of them. As far as short routes are concerned, there are three ways in which he can reach school by using only three pedestrian crossings.

8 · The Sweepstake

Under the set of conditions laid down, the winnings must have been at least:

> Phil . . . £21,
> Paul and Jack . . . £7 each, and
> Dave . . . £5.

9 · Straightforward !

So long as the proprietors of the Kennels did not worry overmuch about the equitable distribution of the space around the individual kennels in the Small Meadow, a mere five fences would be sufficient, as shown in the diagram below.

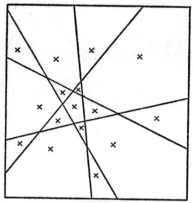

Figure 7

10 · Square Trouble

(i) If the penultimate digit of a square number is odd, then the final digit in the square root of that number must be either 4 or 6. In either of these cases, the final digit of Tom's problem-number must be 6.

(ii) The number now stands as * 3 9 4 2 7 5 6. Now, the sum of the digits of any square number must finally reduce to 1, 4, 7 or 9. Consequently, in the case in point, the only possible figure to have at the front of the number must be 1.

11 · Jobs for the Boys

There are various ways in which this little problem may be tackled, but this is probably the simplest. Assume that *x* men go from Catterley to Royley, and that *y* men go from Catterley to Tripping. From this, the rest of the numbers may be worked out, as shown in the diagram.

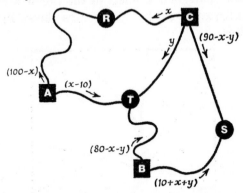

Figure 8

Hence, we can deduce that the total number of miles travelled will be given by the relationship

$$6400 - 10 \, (x + y)$$

and since $(x + y)$ can be only 80 at the most (otherwise men would be coming *from* Tripping *to* Barham, for example) this means that the minimum number of miles travelled must be $6400 - 800$, or *5600*.

12 · Canned

(i) If Barry was in a hurry, the best way to pour would be as follows:

	Alan	Barry	Charles	David
At start:	7	0	0	0
After 1 pouring:	1	6	0	0
,, 2 ,,	1	1	5	0
,, 3 ,,	1	1	1	4
,, 4 ,,	2	1	0	4
,, 5 ,,	2	1	4	0
,, 6 ,,	0	1	4	2

In other words, a total of six pourings would be required in order to effect the required distribution.

(ii) If Barry was in no hurry, then the work could be expedited somewhat . . .

	Alan	Barry	Charles	David
At start:	7	0	0	0
After 1 pouring:	1	6	0	0
,, 2 ,,	1	2	0	4
,, 3 ,,	1	2	4	0
,, 4 ,,	1	0	4	2
,, 5 ,,	0	1	4	2

. . . achieving the desired result after only five pourings.

13 · Knotted or Not?

It will be found that the string in Fig. A is knotted, whereas the one in Fig. B is not.

14 · Cheers!

The only possible arrangement is:

$$
\begin{array}{r}
9228 \\
+\ 9228 \\
\hline
18456
\end{array}
$$

15 · Birthday Bike

The motor-cycle travelled twice as fast as the bus; so had Tim returned by the bus route, without mishap, the trip would have taken 20 minutes. But he took 40 minutes—15 for repairs, 25 travelling. The extra 3 miles were therefore covered in 5 minutes; and in all he must have ridden 5 times 3 miles, *or 15 miles.*

16 · A Weighty Problem

Joe really was extremely lucky—he would only have had to buy one extra weight, and that need only have been of 1 oz. The only trouble would have been that in order to weigh 11 oz., say, he would have had to place the 8 oz. and the 4 oz. weights on the scale, and a 1 oz. weight on the other scale with the goods.

With this extra weight, he would have been able to weigh any whole number of ounces up to and including 1 lb. 14 oz.

17 · Sharing

 (i) Miss Thompson need only make four cuts, though

it must be admitted that some of the children could scarcely be blamed if they did get a little upset about the inequality of the sizes of the various pieces resulting.

(ii) Had the apple been cored, Miss Thompson could conceivably have obtained as many as 18 pieces.

18 · Mathemanian Railways

The rather complicated-looking map shown in the text may be replaced, quite validly, by the diagram shown below.

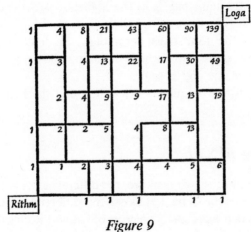

Figure 9

The number which has been placed by each junction indicates the possible number of routes by which the train could reach the junction from Rithm, and is obtained by simply adding the numbers on the junctions previous to it. Hence, there are 139 possible routes which may be taken before the two towns.

[73]

19 · Slot Machines

Although practicalities would probably interfere, there is no mathematical reason why coins for use in slot machines should not have 3, 5, 7, 9, 11, 13, 15, or any other *odd* number of curves or 'sides'.

20 · Eleven Bags Full

There is no reason to use any more than *three* weighings in order to discover the light bag.

For example:

Weigh any four bags against another four. If the scales tip, then the light bag is in the higher scale; if the scales balance, it is in the unweighed bags.

Taking the four bags containing the light bag, and weigh two against two—this will narrow the field to one of two bags in the higher scale.

Weigh the two against each other, and the light one is found.

21 · Age of Sail

However old the two men are, the difference between their ages remains the same. Let us call this difference x years. At one time Ben was exactly twice as old as was Richard; so at that time Richard must have been x years old, and Ben $2x$, and $2x$ is also the age Richard will reach in ten years' time.

Consequently, at the moment Richard must be $2x - 10$ years old, and his father $3x - 10$. Their combined ages come to 125; so we can say that:

$$(2x - 10) + (3x - 10) = 125$$

Hence, x must be 29 years, which in turn means that Richard's age is 48, and his father's is 77.

22 · Wrong Paper

Altogether, there are 24 different ways in which the papers could be delivered to the four houses. Of these, there is 1 way in which all the papers would be delivered correctly, 6 in which two papers would reach the correct destination, and 8 times only one of the readers would have the right paper. This leaves 9 ways in which the papers could all be wrongly delivered.

23 · Escape Bid !

Having had his chat with Alan today, Paul would have to wait for another thirteen days before having another chance to talk to him.

23a · Socks !

Altogether, there are 14,950 different ways in which four socks could be taken from the drawer at random. Of this number, 3,838 ways would result in two pairs of socks being drawn (e.g. one white pair, and one grey). In other words, the odds are slightly better than one in four.

For the benefit of those readers with tidy minds, who would like to see both twins wearing socks of the same colour, the chances of drawing four socks of the same colour from the drawer are:

> 495 for all blue,
> 70 for all grey, and
> 15 for all white,

giving odds of something in the region of 26 to 1 against.

23b · Little Dogies

According to the conditions stated, Chuck must have started with a herd of eight cattle, and the party at which his ranch-hand got drunk must have been held to celebrate Chuck's eighth round-up.

24 · The Flirt

Joe's weekly time-table, as far as his girl-friends were concerned, must follow this pattern:

Monday	Susan
Tuesday	Mary
Wednesday	Anne
Thursday	June
Friday	Pauline
Saturday	Karen

25 · Happy Families

   (i) Karen is Mrs. D. Palster.
  (ii) Eric Tawley is the archer.
 (iii) Paul Elton is the doctor.
 (iv) The doctor's sport is golf.
  (v) Sarah Tawley is the policeman's wife.
 (vi) Mr. Palster's name is Desmond.
(vii) Desmond is a tailor.
(viii) Paul's wife is Mrs. Ann Elton.

26 · Those Gadabouts

Dick's wife is the redhead.

27 · Big Business

(i) Mr. English is based in Scotland, and is an angler.
(ii) Mr. Scott lives in France, and is an aviator.
(iii) Mr. Ireland is based in Wales, and sails.
(iv) Mr. Francis is the representative in Ireland, and plays tennis.
(v) Mr. Welsh is the rugger player, and is based in England.

28 · Two for the Price of One

The least amount which Mary could have spent on the presents must have been thirteen pounds. However, in the case of her having to pay in ten-pound notes without receiving change, the sum involved must have been thirty pounds.

29 · Marriage Partners

Mary, and Suzanne herself, must have both married bankers; Catherine married the sailor; Clarrie wedded the Judge; and Pauline became the stockbroker's wife.

30 · Crossing the Quaggy

Altogether, the boat will have to make a total of *nine* crossings.

One woman takes her son across, and returns;
Her husband takes her back, and returns;
The two men cross, and the second man returns;
He takes his wife across, and she returns;
She crosses back with her son.

31 · Ring Rivals

In the first week, Jim beat Billy. In the second week, Clive beat Billy. In the third week Billy must have met and beaten Martin. Since Martin was not one of those who won only one contest, he must have beaten Jim. As Jim and Martin were engaged in other bouts in the first and third weeks respectively, they must have met in the second week.

32 · The Fairest of Them All

The prettiest of the trio must be auburn-haired Susan.

33 · Dress Sense

Mrs. Evans and Mrs. Baker are in the same colour, and we are told that Mrs. Baker is in blue. Of the other three ladies, neither Mrs. Carroll nor Mrs. Downes is in black, so Mrs. Archer must be. Since Mrs. Downes cannot be wearing brown she must be in green, and Mrs. Carroll must be dressed in brown.

34 · Police Business

The fair-haired suspect must be Dick Taylor, the baker.

35 · Santa's Sleigh

After a great deal of putting-on and taking-off of harness, Bluebell was finally put in the lead, followed in order by Twinkle, Sugar-lump, Jeremy, Dancer, Snowflake, Prancer and Thunderbird.

36 · Clubland

The total male population of the village of Chessletbury must be 56.

37 · Blondes, Brunettes, or Redheads?

Since those who liked redheads are included among those liking blondes, and since there were only 3 who didn't care for blondes, the total number must have been 25.

As 7 voted 'blondes only', and 6 liked redheads, the balance of the 22 blonde-admirers must consist of 9 who liked both blondes and brunettes; 16 like brunettes, and of these 3 like brunettes only. Taking (9 + 3) from 16, we are left with 4 who like all three types.

38 · Identikit

Mrs. Jackson's assailant was discovered by the police issuing an 'Identikit' picture made up as follows:

Hair	no. 3
Eyebrows	no. 2
Eyes	no. 4
Nose	no. 6
Mouth	no. 2
Chin	no. 1

39 · The New Teacher

With a little thought, Mr. Jones was able to match up his tormentors' names, and duly gave the following list to the Headmaster:

Tom Smith
Susan Jones
Mary Brown
Jim Harris
Charles Robinson

40 · Bridge Fiends

(Although Inspector O'Brien found his first visit to the Bigglesberry Arms a little frustrating at the time, yet the fact that he was able to identify the four men made a very favourable impression on the landlord, who was a considerable power in the locality as well as in the local.)

Joe was the bald undertaker;
Tom was the dark-haired Town Clerk;
Bill was the fair-haired doctor; and
Dennis was the red-haired solicitor.

41 · The Navigators

The final order of the competitors in the Navigation Test was Bill, Eric, Arthur, George, Harry, Dave, Fred and (last, but still happy at having been considered good enough to have been allowed to enter the competition) Charlie.

42 · Double Acrostic (I)

CARPET   carp
            angle
            regiment

43 · Double Acrostic (II)

FOREST   free
                oasis
                riot

44 · Double Acrostic (III)

TYPEWRITER   tear
                     yogi
                     pat
                     erase
                     war

45 · Andrew's Puzzle

FLIPPERS   flop
                  lodge
                  incur
                  puddings

46 · Triple Acrostic

CARPETBAGGER   careering
                        abating
                        reimburse
                        par

47 · Twisted Triple Acrostic

WASHING-MACHINES
wench
atingocni
Simon
htebazilE
Incas

48 · Word Ladders

FOOT	SOOT	SHOT	SHOE	
WOOD	WOOL	COOL	COAL	
FOOT	FOOD	FORD	FARD	YARD
LEAF	LOAF	LOAD	GOAD	GOOD

49 · Vocabulary (I)

```
E NTI RE TY
M ENTA LL Y
E VENTUAL
C EMENTED
P RESENTS
VI RULENT
```

50 · Vocabulary (II)

```
T ONALI TY
S TONEOI L
A STONISH
P LATONI C
OI LSTONE
R EBUTTON
```

51 · Vocabulary (III)

```
M E N T A L I T Y
A M E N D M E N T
D E M E N T A T E
E L E M E N T A L
R U D I M E N T S
S E N T I M E N T
G E N T L E M E N
```

52 · Word Square (I)

```
D O N E
O P U S
N U N S
E S S E
```

53 · Word Square (II)

```
P A N S
A V O N
N O V A
S N A P
```

54 · Word Square (III)

```
E V I L
V I L E
I L L S
L E S S
```

55 · Word Square (IV)

```
S T A M P
T O T A L
A T O N E
M A N T A
P L E A T
```

56 · Word Square (V)

```
P L U M B
L A V E R
U V U L A
M E L O N
B R A N D
```

57 · Word Square (VI)

```
S C O P E
C A P E R
O P E R A
P E R I S
E R A S E
```

58 · Word Square (VII)

```
P L A N T
L A B O R
A B A S E
N O S E S
T R E S S
```

59 · A Square Quotation

'Each in his narrow cell for ever laid,
The rude forefathers of the hamlet sleep.'

60 · Characters

Dennis Wheatley	Roger Brook
Isaac Asimov	The C-chute
Charlotte Bronte	Jane Eyre
Kenneth Grahame	Toad
Edward Lear	The Yonghy-Bonghy-Bo
Noel Coward	Mrs. Worthington
Sax Rohmer	Fu Manchu

61 · Hexagonal Quotation

'Give me chastity and continency
—but not yet.'
(*Confessions*, III, 12)

62 · Colours

Black Arrow	R. L. Stevenson
A Study in Scarlet	Conan Doyle
The Purple Plain	H. E. Bates
The Golden Bough	James G. Frazer
The White Peacock	D. H. Lawrence
The Corn is Green	Emlyn Williams
The Silver Box	John Galsworthy

63 · Numbers

Two on a Tower	T. Hardy
Three Sisters	Chekhov
Four Just Men	Edgar Wallace
The Four Winds of Love	Compton Mackenzie
Anna of the Five Towns	Arnold Bennett
Seven Pillars of Wisdom	T. E. Lawrence
The Thirty-Nine Steps	John Buchan

64 · Tetrahedral Quotation

'When a dog bites a man that is not news,
but when a man bites a dog that is news.'

65 · Nautical Quotation

'There is a tide in the affairs of men,
Which, taken at the flood, leads on to fortune;
Omitted, all the voyage of their life
Is bound in shallows and in miseries.'
  (Shakespeare: *Julius Caesar*, IV, iii, 217)

66 · Dates

The answers to the six questions are:

XM *Alice in Wonderland* made her appearance in 1865.
PR *The Power and the Glory* first appeared in 1940.
RM The 'Saint' made his entrance in 1928.
XP *The Mask of Demetrios* was published in 1939.
MX Rousseau's *Confessions* was published in 1781.
XR The year 1495 saw Denmark produce her first printed book (a rhymed history).

From the above, it will be recognized that the correct route from PR to RP is

PR ... XP ... RM ... RP

67 · Crossword

```
C O P E   L A S T   A C T
O   A V A I L   H   A   D
L O R E   S I L E N T L Y
D   T R I P E   A   C   E
  D   E   S N A T C H E R
P R E S S   S   R   A S S
  E   T E A   Y E S   S
B A G   A   E   S P R A Y
A M A S S I N G   O   Y
M   R   H   I R A T E   S
B A T H O R S E   T A L K
I   E   R   L E V E R   I
  B R I E F E D   D L I T
```

68 · Twisted Crossword

```
P E E L S A   T S I S E R
I   N   P   S   E   L   O
R E S U O R T   S N I K S
A   U   O   I K S   C   T
T N E T N O C   I   K L E
E     R     K   O   E O R
  L A Y O R   K N U R T
R A C   U   V     R     R
E Y L   T   E T A N A M E
V   I   D O R   V   D   T
E C N U O   S S E R D N U
R   I   O   E   R   E   R
S K C A R C   E T I R E N
```

[87]

69 · Clueless

70 · Reversals

71 · Hidden Countries

'When you hear that a friend has developed swoll*en gland*s or some such thing, and has had to enter hosp*ital*, *y*ou tend to forget that there are more comfortable places to be ill in. For example, some people go to *spa in* search of health—though this is really feasible only when one happens to own a ban*k, or ea*rns enough to keep half the female population of New York *in dia*monds.'

72 · Matchsticks

With the use of a few dabs of glue, and a little imagination, forty-five squares may be constructed.

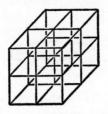

73 · More Matchsticks

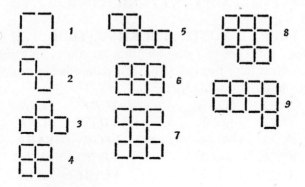

74 · The End !

FPGP   Biannual.
XDYC   Knotted.

YCHH	Not unique. The two possible solutions are:

9831	9841
941	931
10772	10772

FCPY	Both answers are correct.
YCKH	Traitor.
XCPY	True (618000 casualties, as compared to 116516).
XBPY	True.
FPDH	No. For example, the Moebius Strip illustrated here:

YBGP	No (if a man is a widower, his wife is in no position to marry anyone).
XPYC	Both answers are correct.

From the above, the correct route may be seen to be:

FCPY . . . XCPY . . . YCKH . . . YBGP . . . E

or it may be

FCPY . . . XDYC . . . YCKH . . . YBGP . . . E.

Since there are two possible 'shortest routes', my sister Anne must have five children, their names being those in italics in the following list:

XBPY	JOAN	*XCPY*	*JEAN*
XPYC	JANE	*XDYC*	*JUNE*
FCPY	*SEAN*	FPGP	SARA
FPDH	SAUL	*YBGP*	*NORA*
YCKH	*NEIL*	YCHH	NELL